PANIC CYCLE

TRIGGER
(external/internal

BEHAVIOUR
(AVOID)

selective
attention

EMOTION

Negative
THOUGHT

PHYSICAL
SYMPTOMS
(Heart racing)

ANXIETY
(FEAR)

RETHINKING
ANXIETY

MARGARET BRISTOW

SM**5**OTH
STONES

Copyright © 2012 by Margaret Bristow, All rights reserved.
No portion of this book may be reproduced, stored in a retrieval system, or transmitted in any form or by any means – electronic, mechanical, photocopy, recording, or any other – except for brief quotations in printed reviews, without the prior permission of the publisher.

First published in Great Britain by 5 Smooth Stones
102 Queslett Road East, Streetly, B74 2EZ

Unless otherwise indicated, Scripture quotations used in this book are from The New International Version, Copyright © 1978 by New York International Bible Society

Cover design concept by Phil Bristow
Design concept and development by Affi Luc Agbodo

A CIP catalogue record for this title is available from the British Library.
ISBN-10: 0-9563342-2-9
ISBN-13: 978-0-9563342-2-0

Printed in the United States of America.

Acknowledgments

I especially thank Phil my husband and very best friend for always inspiring me, believing in me, supporting and encouraging me– I wouldn't have done it without you.

My daughters Claire and Rebecca and my sons-in-law Michael and Dom who have listened and so faithfully encouraged me in this task – thank you.

To friends who have been there to read, edit and cheer me on, especially Affi Luc Agbodo who has given so much time in helping to publish this workbook – thank you.

Preface

As a child I loved to watch the butterflies on the buddleia tree and hated to see one caught in a spiders web, immobilised and unable to fly away to freedom.

I always wanted to know what could be done to set these butterflies free from the webs. I soon discovered that I, as a person, also needed to be set free from the cobwebs of life and so started my quest to discover the truth to be found in Jesus.

The topic of *Anxiety* is close to my heart because I firmly believe that as we understand and experience more of the truth of God's love we will be increasingly free from the webs of fear and anxiety.

My journey has included working as an occupational therapist on locked wards in mental health hospitals, Social Services and Secondary NHS mental health teams. I have also worked as a volunteer for charities in the U.K., Switzerland, Pakistan and Hong Kong. I have learned that we all, at times, struggle with anxiety to one degree or another.

The concepts and strategies in the modules have been developed from both a Biblical and primarily cognitive behaviour therapy model. They include practical strategies and techniques that can be applied personally in one's relationship with God and then to daily living activities.

The approach is based on the theory that Generalised Anxiety is a result of problematic, negative thinking and that targeting cognitions, the thinking process and behaviours as part of a daily relationship with our Heavenly Father can bring healing and help people manage their anxiety responses.

While wanting to provide information about anxiety, it is important to state that the diagnosis and treatment of acute anxiety or associated mental illnesses does require the attention of a General Practitioner or properly qualified mental health professional. The information in these modules is not a substitute for proper diagnosis, treatment or the provision of advice by appropriate health professionals.

The information in these modules has been developed for information and is not a series of therapy session for anxiety.

Rethinking Anxiety is a practical workbook, which offers the reader opportunities to recognise, consider and rethink the unhelpful thought patterns that can lead to anxiety. Within each of the five modules there are helpful *tasks* and *home activity* to work through before moving to the next module.

My hope is that this book will be used as an aid to help release people from the webs of fear and anxiety that have prevented them from flying away to freedom.

Margaret Bristow

Then you will know the truth and the truth will set you free.

John 8:32

"We walk in circles, so limited by our own anxieties that we can no longer distinguish between true and false."

– Ingrid Bergman

Content

Acknowledgement iii

Preface v

Introduction xi

Module 1 17
Overview of anxiety

Module 2 45
The physical effects of anxiety, panic and behaviours
that maintain the anxiety response

Module 3 75
The role of behaviour in the anxiety response

Module 4 103
Understanding how thinking affects anxiety

Module 5 127
Challenging unhelpful thinking and problem solving

Conclusion 149

Personal Future Anxiety Management plan 150

Introduction

We increasingly live in an anxious society where lives often feel so 'overstretched' and burdened with expectation that it becomes difficult to balance work and home life. Many lives have become dominated by fear; fear of unemployment, fear of not being able to pay bills, fear of sickness or loneliness, and the list goes on.

The rate of common mental disorders, typically depression and anxiety, has risen. The World Health Organisation estimates that by 2020 depression alone will be the second biggest ailment in the world after heart disease. [1] Most work institutions are afflicted by a climate of anxiety, including the Church.

It is important to recognise that anxiety is a multidimensional state, in which spiritual, social, psychological and physical factors all play a role in its cause or origin.

As individual Christians and as the 'family of God' we are not exempt from anxiety and being dominated by fear; fear of holding slightly different views, fear of speaking out

---

[1] Yves Lecrubier (2003) 'The burden of Depression and Anxiety in General Medicine' *Official Journal of the World Psychiatric Association.* 2 (3) p162

individually and collectively, fear of persecution, fear of being different, or fear of failure. It is important that the Church is not ignorant of the impact of mental illness, and the detrimental effect it can have on individuals, families and society. Jesus' ministry was all about his loving relationship with mankind and included healing the unwell both physically and mentally. The message conveyed by the New Testament is that the Kingdom of God actively demonstrates the healing power of God.

As a church we surely need to be creative in providing the interpersonal dynamic of a loving caring atmosphere that includes a culture of respect and honour, and an environment that reduces the stigma associated with mental health issues – where people can admit without guilt that they have anxieties or other problems and receive help.

We need to remember that while the Bible challenges us not to be anxious this is not to provoke guilt and make us feel worse about how we perceive ourselves. The aim is to learn to 'cast' our anxiety upon God and to find healing from our deepest fears. This is part of the process of renewing our minds. *Romans 12:1*

The anxiety modules aim to provide a significant step in this direction. At any point in these modules, the person confronting anxiety can identify progress toward restoration by referring to the Recovery Curve diagram.

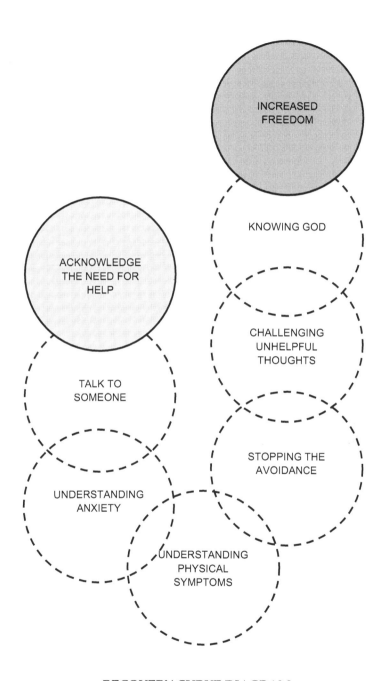

RECOVERY CURVE DIAGRAM

ACKNOWLEDGE THE NEED FOR HELP – It is vital for us to know that it is okay to seek help for anxiety and acknowledge that the anxiety is affecting daily living activities and relationships.

TALK TO SOMEONE – By telling the personal story related to anxiety one may start to gain insight into its origin and what maintains it.

UNDERSTANDING ANXIETY – To start to tell someone and to prayerfully talk to God about how anxiety affects daily life and relationships starts the process of breaking the denial about suffering from anxiety and setting the 'captive free' from the fear(s) behind the anxiety.

UNDERSTANDING PHYSICAL SYMPTOMS – When we feel anxious a chain of automatic responses occur in our bodies

STOPPING THE AVOIDANCE – As part of this process it is important to have people to talk and pray with, to have people who will lovingly support us and if necessary to challenge us especially when we are avoiding certain daily living activities.

CHALLENGING UNHELPFUL THOUGHTS – It is important to identify our negative thinking styles and challenge our unhelpful thinking in order to reduce our anxiety symptoms.

KNOWING GOD – This is a journey of knowing who God is and who we are in relationship with a loving Heavenly Father who wants his children to find acceptance and healing restoration.

INCREASED FREEDOM – As a result of the journey of 'casting all our cares' on God and of being able to face each day knowing more of God while in the centre of the anxious trials of life, we can find freedom.

Module 1

Overview of Anxiety

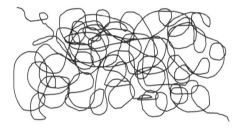

"I am an old man and have known a great many troubles, but most of them never happened."

– Mark Twain

Introduction   19

Typical words and sentences used by
people suffering from anxiety   20

What is anxiety?   21

The Bible and anxiety   22

Types of anxiety   25

What causes anxiety?   27

How does anxiety affect you?   30

My anxiety cycle   35

What maintains anxiety?   40

Home activity   42

Summary   44

Introduction

The aim of this module is to provide you with some information about anxiety, to describe the types of symptoms common to anxiety and to discuss what maintains anxiety.

Exercise task 1

Think of the symptoms that describe anxiety for you. This may include physical symptoms, thoughts or images or emotional responses.

Physical symptoms:

....

....

....

....

Thoughts / images that pass through your mind:

....

....

....

....

Emotions:

....

....

....

....

Typical words and sentences used by people suffering from anxiety

WORRIED – PANICKY – NERVOUS – TENSE

STRESSED OUT – ON EDGE – UNABLE TO RELAX

'WHAT IF' …

Here are some typical examples of what people with anxiety have said:

"I worry about everything. I get tense and wound up, and end up shouting at the children."

"My mouth is dry and it is hard to swallow properly and then I begin to get panicky. I think I am going to stop breathing."

"Even before I get there I start to think of all the things that might go wrong. When I arrive my heart starts to pound, my legs turn to jelly and I just know I am going to make a fool of myself. I just have to get out"

"My mind starts to race, I feel like I am going to lose control and go mad or something."

As we can see from the above sentences anxiety symptoms will include physical responses: dry mouth, increased heart rate, sweating, rapid breathing, fear of passing out, nausea; alongside alteration in thought processing, accompanied by the emotional response of fear.

What is Anxiety?

Everybody experiences general feelings of nervousness or a sense of being worried about something. For some though, the worry or feeling of anxiety can start to take over their lives. It is thought that 1 in 20 people experience significant anxiety at some point in their lives. It is important to remember you are not alone!

Understanding Anxiety

When we are anxious we are afraid. FEAR is a survival instinct, which occurs in response to a realistically dangerous situation. When we feel anxious a chain of automatic events is occurring in our bodies, which prepares us for action.

If approached by a dangerous wild animal you would most likely respond with fear. This reaction is termed the 'flight or fight' response. It is our body preparing for action either to fight or to run from danger. It is important that we do respond with fear at times like this because as we become afraid it triggers an automatic response in our bodies and we begin to experience the 'arousal reaction', we begin to be physically prepared to defend ourselves from danger. Anxiety can be experienced in less threatening situations. For example going for an interview, candidates will feel some degree of anxiety. This response is part of the process of survival. In certain situations this can be a definite advantage. It means you are ready for action and it enables you to respond quickly if necessary. Anxiety is a normal response at times of perceived danger or in worrying situations.

Anxiety only becomes a problem when it is so extreme that it interferes with our performance, when it is out of proportion to the situation, when it occurs in situations where there is no actual threat. When it is at this level it starts to interfere with daily living activities, for example becoming anxious when shopping at the supermarket.

The Bible and Anxiety

It is really important at the outset to recognise that God cares for us and loves us, anxious or not.

Psalm 8:4 says, "What is man that you are mindful of him, the son of man that you care for him?" (New International version)

In *Ephesians 3:16* we learn that God wants to strengthen our inner person, that we might be rooted and established in love knowing how wide and long and high and deep the love of Christ is, and that we might know this love that surpasses knowledge, that each person might feel increasingly secure in his love. The Bible tells us that the more we know God's love the less we will fear.

But perfect love drives out fear. (*1 John 4:18*)

Recognising that anxiety is a fear response the Bible has some 365 references relating directly or indirectly to fear, one for each day of the year! These range from 'do not be afraid' to 'do not fear' to 'do not let your hearts be troubled'.

As Christians we need to recognise that we have an enemy who does not want us to be at peace, one of the tactics of our enemy Satan, the 'accuser', is to bring fear and anxiety but God is on our side!

In *Proverbs 12:25* we learn that 'an anxious heart weighs a man down' and in *Matthew 6:25* we are told not to worry about our lives. *Philippians 4:6* says 'Do not be anxious about anything!'

But the reality is that we do get anxious!

The problem is that we can quickly get into a guilt trip about being anxious and feel condemned and ashamed 'I must be the worst Christian because I'm so anxious and what would (X) say about me if they knew?' As a result we feel even more anxious and are tempted not to tell anyone. This may result in a low mood.

We need to recognise that we are imperfect and our human condition prevents us from attaining the complete peace that every Christian aspires to. However, God has made provision for this!

1 Peter 5:7 says, 'Cast all your anxiety on him because he cares for you.'

This is the starting place for dealing with our anxiety. It is about getting to know more of God's love that dispels fear, acknowledging our anxiety and asking Him to come and help us in the midst of the anxiety!

ACTION: Pray for the 'journey' of handling anxiety!

- Take some time with God.

- Thank Him that he cares for you and that he loves you.

- Start to admit to yourself that you are anxious and fearful.

- Perhaps make a list of all the things that you are anxious about and seek God's help asking that He strengthen you as you start this journey of becoming less anxious.

- If you are feeling brave seek out a friend and ask them to start praying for you or even with you!!

Exercise Task 2

I am anxious about

....

....

....

I am going to seek help and talk to:

....

Types of Anxiety

Anxiety can be experienced in different ways. It may be helpful to be able to distinguish the different types of anxiety.

- Remembering that anxiety is a response to FEAR sometimes the fear occurs in response to specific things: objects, spiders, snakes, water, heights etc. These fears are called phobias.

- Other people experience fear in social situations or at the thought of a social situation. This is called social anxiety.

- Others experience fear that is sudden in onset. These are known as panic attacks.

- Generalised anxiety is when someone has a lot of anxiety; feeling fearful or worried on most days. The anxiety may be about stress at work or at home and can be about minor things. The sufferer may not know why they are anxious though the distress will be affecting their daily activities.

Normal anxiety becomes a problem when:

1. It is out of proportion,
2. It feels out of control,
3. It is persistent (for at least 6 months),
4. It is intrusive in your life and impairs your daily activities,
5. It causes significant distress.

Generalised anxiety will pervade a number of different areas such as health, work, finances, or relationships. It is not specific as with the other anxieties. It is not uncommon for people suffering with generalised anxiety to also experience other types of anxiety or mood disorders such as depression.

Exercise task 3

To help you consider if you need to take action think about how serious your generalised anxiety is, try rating the following two questions.

How distressing is your generalised anxiety? (Circle the number describing you.)

1	2	3	4	5	6	7	8	9	10

1 = Not at all   5 = Moderately   10 = Extremely

How much does your generalised anxiety interfere with daily living? (Circle the number describing you.)

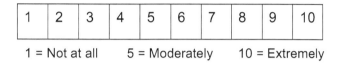

1	2	3	4	5	6	7	8	9	10

1 = Not at all   5 = Moderately   10 = Extremely

(If scoring 7 and above it is advisable to contact a health professional, such as your G.P.)

What causes Anxiety?

There can be a number of vulnerabilities that increase the chance of developing anxiety.

Biological factors

There can be an inherited general disposition; tendency towards experiencing negative emotions. A person's body arousal response might be triggered more quickly and take longer to calm down. However, no single gene has been associated with generalised anxiety.

Psychological factors

The life style of a person, the types of life stressors a person has encountered and how they have coped with such stressors will increase vulnerability to anxiety. Prolonged stress and past experiences of trauma or uncontrollable negative experiences are of significance. As a result of life experiences people may come to believe that life is dangerous and unpredictable. Direct and indirect messages from others as role models can cause people to believe that the world is an unsafe place and that worrying is useful. They may think that worry helps them achieve a greater sense of certainty because they would be better prepared for anything.

A coping style that includes a person regularly avoiding situations where there is a possibility of experiencing negative emotions can increase the likelihood for anxiety.

Spiritual factors

We need to acknowledge as Christians that all or part of the above may apply to us and we also have an enemy 'Satan', the 'accuser' who the Bible informs us comes as a 'thief' seeking to harm us and our relationship with God, whereas Jesus comes to bring life in fullness.

'The thief comes only to steal and kill and destroy; I have come that you may have life, and have it to the full.' (*John 10:10*)

Here are some of the common underlying beliefs in generalised anxiety:

About 'SELF': One's beliefs may tend to centre on personal weakness and vulnerability.

About 'OTHERS': Tend to believe others are strong, but unreliable in terms of 'being there' for you personally.

About the 'WORLD': Tend to view the world as a dangerous and unpredictable place.

About 'GOD': Beliefs about failing God, not being good enough or coming up to standard, perhaps that God has abandoned us. Often there is a wrong understanding of God's character. There may be anger toward God.

Exercise task 4

Think about what causes your anxiety.

Belief's about 'one's self:

....

Belief's about 'others':

....

Belief's about the 'world':

....

Belief's about 'God':

....

Diagnosis and treatment of generalised anxiety

Generalised anxiety is not always easy to diagnose as some of the symptoms overlap with those of depression and other anxiety problems. It is important to see a mental health professional for a definite diagnosis and treatment.

How does anxiety affect you?

Anxiety can affect us in five different ways. It affects:

1. The way we respond in our emotions
2. The way our bodies physically react
3. The way we think
4. The way we behave
5. The way we relate to God

Exercise task 5

To help identify your symptoms of anxiety, place a tick next to those symptoms you experience regularly.

1. How you feel emotionally

Anxious	
Nervous	
Worried	
Frightened	

Irritable	
Feeling something dreadful will happen	
Tense	
Stressed	
Uptight	
Unsettled	
Panicky	
Other	

2. What happens to your body? (Physical response)

Heart pounding or racing	
Chest tight or painful	
Tingling or numbness in fingers or toes	
Stomach churching or butterflies	
Having to go to the toilet frequently	
Feeling jumpy or restless	
Tense muscles	
Body aching	
Dizzy or light headed	

Sweating	
Other	

3. How do you think?

Constant worrying	
Can't concentrate	
Thoughts racing	
Imagining the worst and dwelling on it	
Mind jumping from one thing to another	
Other	

Common thoughts might be!

"I'm losing control", "I'm cracking up"

"I'm going to faint", "My legs will give way"

"I'm going to have a heart attack"

"I'm going to make a fool of myself"

"I can't cope", "I have to get out of here"

4. What you do (Behaviour)

Pace up and down	
On the go all the time	
Talk quickly or more than usual	
Snappy and irritable behaviour	
Drinking more	
Smoke more	
Eat more or less	
Avoid situations	
Other	

5. The way you relate to God

Avoid relationship with God by not praying	
Avoid other Christians	
Not letting others know how debilitating your anxiety is resulting in secrecy and emotions of shame and guilt	
By being angry with God – "Why is this happening to me, it's not fair."	
Thinking that God is punishing you, or it's your fault	

There is a sense of God being distant	
Other	

Other responses

....

....

....

If you are regularly experiencing some or all of these symptoms, then it is possible that you are suffering from anxiety and it is recommended that you seek medical advice. If you are a Christian try and find someone who you can talk to about your anxiety symptoms remembering that God loves you and many believers battle with anxiety – you are not alone! What keeps you alone is FEAR!

My anxiety cycle

The diagram depicts the five ways in which anxiety affects a person.

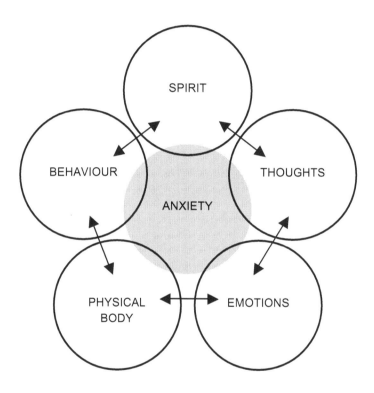

DIAGRAM MODEL OF ANXIETY

Exercise task 6

THE ANXIETY RESPONSE – 'Mrs Apple'

Mrs Apple has been a Christian for a long time. She has two children and has worked as a receptionist for 5 years. Now as an adult Mrs Apple realises anxiety was a part of the family home as a child; her mother would anxiously wait at the front window watching for her husband to return home each evening from work on his bicycle; there had been anxiety as a child regarding finances; her mother's physical health had been poor and her father was a very strict authoritarian figure. Mrs Apple had coped with this as a child considering it part of 'normal life.'

At work Mrs Apple has never had any complaints about her abilities or her work performance. She generally enjoys her job but frequently gets anxious whilst at work and is increasingly concerned about her anxiety symptoms.

Mrs Apple has told none of her Christian friends about her anxiety because she fears they may judge her and just tell her to trust God. Mrs Apple herself increasingly feels guilty as a Christian for her anxiety thinking that she mustn't be good enough or that she is failing to trust God enough. She has gradually started to avoid church because of her anxiety symptoms.

At work Mrs Apple organises the room bookings for the 'Boardroom' that several companies share within the same building. The 'Board room' is frequently booked for appointments one after the other. Quite often one of the company managers, Mr Plum, stays in the booked room too long or will use the room without checking with Mrs Apple if it is already booked. This causes trouble with other company managers who are kept waiting to use the room.

Mrs Apple always avoids telling Mr Plum that he needs to vacate the room because she thinks he may shout at her and think her to be incompetent. Instead Mrs Apple repeatedly apologises to the other angry company managers and feels guilty about the situation. Mrs Apple notices that her heart races and she sweats at the thought of approaching Mr Plum.

When she goes home she tells herself, "you should have spoken to Mr Plum, you are so stupid and just weak." Mrs Apple feels sad and worries about what the other managers think about her.

When she thinks about praying and talking to God about it she feels condemned and a failure and keeps worrying about what other people would think of her if they knew how anxious she was. When she gets up for work she feels anxious as she thinks of the day ahead. She dreads confronting Mr Plum and repeatedly tells herself "you really messed up again".

Considering the origins and causes of Anxiety can you identify what had made Mrs Apple vulnerable to anxiety?

....
....
....
....

Remembering the 'anxiety' diagram model and the five areas in which anxiety can affect a person's life, answer the following questions.

What was making Mrs Apple anxious?

Can you identify her thoughts?
....
....

Can you spot what her physical responses were?

....
....

Can you identify what she was feeling emotionally?

....
....

How did the circumstances affect her behaviour?

....

....

How was her anxiety affecting her relationship with God?

....

....

Exercise task 7

My personal anxiety response: Notice how anxiety takes centre stage

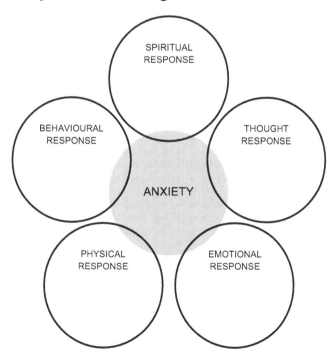

What maintains Anxiety?

Someone might be a 'worrier'

Worrying is "self talk" that includes "what if" questions where the person has an internal dialogue about the things they fear might happen. Remember Mrs Apple's mother standing at the window waiting for her husband to come home? Her "what if" question might have been, "what if he gets knocked off his bicycle how will I ever manage financially to look after the children?" The internal conversation will be about possible future events that might happen and of which we are afraid. We will repeatedly discuss the event with ourselves and think how we might deal with it. In this process people are often left thinking that they will be unable to cope with the future.

Ongoing stresses

Some people have ongoing stresses over a number of years, which means they can develop the habit of being anxious.

Vicious cycle of anxiety

The physical symptoms of anxiety can be frightening. People often react by thinking that there is something physically wrong with them or that something really awful is going to happen to them; "I'm going to have a heart attack." This can cause more anxious thinking and more physical symptoms and so a vicious cycle develops.

Fear of fear

Someone who has experienced anxiety in a particular situation in the past may start to predict feeling anxious, and become frightened of the symptoms themselves, this in turn causes the very symptoms that are feared.

Avoidance

When a vicious cycle has developed, with lots of anxious thoughts increasing the anxiety symptoms, avoidance may be used as a way of coping with the anxiety, like Mrs Apple avoiding confronting Mr Plum.

It is very natural to avoid situations that we perceive as dangerous. However, those suffering with anxiety tend to avoid situations that often do not hold real dangers, such as crowded places, buses or perhaps talking to people. Not only are these situations not dangerous but they are also necessary. This can result in a loss of confidence, which in turn makes a person more anxious.

HOME ACTIVITY

TASK 1: KEEP A DIARY

What situations made you anxious, were you at home, at work, a prayer meeting?

....
....
....

How did you respond physically?

....
....
....

How were you feeling emotionally?

....
....
....

What were you thinking about / what images did you have?

....
....
....

What did you do? Was it helpful? (Behaviours)

....
....
....

How did it affect your relationship with God?

....

....

....

TASK 2: KEEP A DIARY

Review the Bible verses used in module 1 or choose others that will help you consider God's love and acceptance of you.

Psalm 8:4 – Ephesians 3:16 – 1John 4:18 – Proverbs 12:25

Matthew 6:25 – Philippians 4:6 – Peter 5:7 – John 10:10

Summary of module 1

- Anxiety and worry is a normal experience, it is the body's normal response to threat or danger. Anxiety is not dangerous.

- Anxiety becomes a problem when the symptoms are severe, persistent and are out of proportion to the perceived danger.

- Anxiety often becomes a vicious circle where the symptoms, thoughts and behaviour keep the anxiety going.

- Anxiety affects our daily relationships and our relationship with God. By 'casting' our anxiety on Him we can find new security and a refuge from all our fear(s). It is a journey that starts by seeking help.

Module 2

The physical effects of anxiety, panic and behaviours that maintain the anxiety response

"Worry never robs tomorrow of its sorrows, it only saps today of its joys."

- Leo Buscaglia

Introduction   47

Firm foundations and letting God in   49

Physical response to anxiety   52

Physical response to panic   52

How anxiety and panic are maintained
by our behaviour   58

How to handle panic attacks   62

How we breathe in anxiety and panic
attacks   65

Relaxation skills   67

When panic occurs   70

Home Activity   72

Summary   73

Introduction

The aim of this module is to provide an understanding of the physical effects of the 'flight/fight' response in anxiety and panic, which is based on fear.

To understand anxiety and panic we need to understand FEAR.

A dictionary definition of fear is: 'painful emotion caused by impending danger or evil, a state of alarm.' (Concise Oxford dictionary) The Vine's Bible dictionary describes *"fear"*, *fearful, fearfulness* as linked with 'flight'; as that which is caused by being scared, in dread, terror, and is caused by intimidation of adversaries. The Bible in *2 Timothy 1:7* tells us that God did not give us a spirit of fear, fearfulness, or timidity. In the introduction to the course we spoke of how Satan, the 'accuser' wants people to live in fear.

The key is that God has made each of us to have deep spiritual needs: The two greatest commandments describe the need to love and be loved, which provides us with a deep sense of security that dispels fear. This sense of being loved brings self worth and gives us a loving purpose in life. (*Matthew 22: 37-39*) Not to have our personal need for love met causes underlying fear, which we may not be consciously aware of.

Anxiety results when these spiritual needs are not being met in an appropriate way. Often we try to fulfil these needs by using inappropriate coping methods. Rather than trusting in God we build our own cisterns/systems that leak, do not work effectively or put our trust in strategies to protect ourselves. (*Jeremiah 2:13 or Psalm 20:7*)

For example consider all the different behaviours employed to maintain a good 'self image'; we work extra hard to achieve approval from significant others; we compete to look the best; we become people pleasers to gain praise. Not to build these cisterns/systems would mean we would be vulnerable to the fear of not being acceptable, loveable, good enough. It is when these systems or strategies are employed to extremes, or when we can no longer maintain them that they fail. Fear emerges and results in anxiety and panic responses.

The need to be loved is the basis for many people's anxiety. Someone may perceive a situation threatening because it requires a high level of expectation of themselves; the higher the expectation and the more serious the threat the greater the anxiety.

Firm foundations and letting God in

It is important to commence module 2 on a firm foundation of understanding the truth of who we are in relationship with God and to invite Jesus into the centre of our fears.

Exercise task 1

Whilst remembering that God's love drives out fear it is important to understand more of what the Bible says about the **TRUTH** of how God sees those who love him and are loved by him. This does not depend upon how we emotionally 'feel'.

I am accepted: I am no longer rejected or unloved. In Christ I am completely accepted.

God says:

John 1:12 – I am God's child.

John 15:15 – As a disciple, I am a friend of Jesus Christ.

Ephesians 1: 3-8 – I have been chosen by God and adopted as his child.

1 Corinthians 6: 19 – I have been bought with a price. I belong to God.

I am secure: I am no longer unprotected, alone or abandoned. In Christ I am secure.

God says:

Romans 8: 31-39 - I cannot be separated from the love of God.

2 Timothy 1:7 – I have not been given a spirit of fear but of power, love and a sound mind.

I am significant: I am no longer worthless, inadequate or hopeless. In Christ I am deeply significant and special.

God says:

Ephesians 2:10 – I am God's workmanship.

Ephesians 3:12 – I may approach God with freedom and confidence.

Ephesians 2:6 – I am seated with Christ in the heavenly realms.

Exercise task 2

It is important to ask Jesus to come into the very centre of your fears and anxiety and even the deep sense of panic that attacks!

Consider Matthew 8:24

The disciples are in their boat when the storm comes without warning and it is terrifying, life threatening – as panic can seem.

- Where is Jesus in the anxiety / panic of the disciples?
- What action did the disciples take?
- How intense is your anxiety and panic – do you feel you will drown?
- Where is Jesus?
- What action will you take?
- What action did Jesus take when with the disciples?
- What did he say to their anxiety storm?
- What does Jesus say to your anxiety storm?
- What are you afraid of?

As you have asked Jesus into the centre of your fear or panic attacks ask someone to pray with you about the fear behind them.

Physical response to anxiety

In the last module we described how when we feel anxious a chain of automatic responses occurs in our bodies, which prepares us for action. The reaction is to fight, to take flight or indeed to freeze. This survival response automatically occurs in the face of approaching or perceived danger. As a result of this automatic response the body experiences the "arousal reaction."

Physical response to panic

Sometimes it is possible to have this intense surge of *FEAR* response when there is no danger; it is a false alarm! This is the same response that you might have in response to realistic danger but it happens in situations that most people are not afraid about. Many people experience mild sensations when they feel anxious but in a panic attack it is sudden in onset. Many of the symptoms are similar to anxiety and the symptoms peak within 10 minutes. These symptoms can be terrifying and there may be a strong desire to flee the situation or seek medical assistance due to the fear of physical harm, for example a heart attack.

Panic disorder describes the condition where panic attacks happen unexpectedly rather than in predictable situations. Panic attacks can occur unexpectedly, which causes distress.

People with panic disorder have a persistent anxiety, or fear of having another panic attack, or worry about the consequences of the panic attack.

People will change their behaviour in the attempt to prevent the onset of panic and may begin to avoid any place they cannot escape from with ease.

People with phobias may have a panic attack in relation to the feared object or situation.

It is important that if these symptoms persist and are severe, the person is assessed by a qualified health professional to ensure the correct diagnosis.

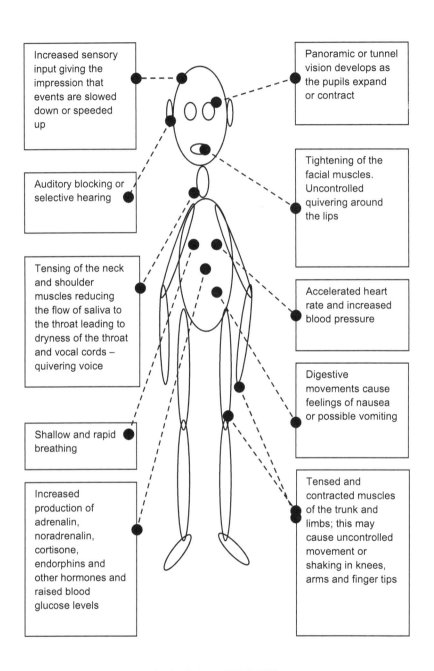

Increased sensory input giving the impression that events are slowed down or speeded up

Panoramic or tunnel vision develops as the pupils expand or contract

Auditory blocking or selective hearing

Tightening of the facial muscles. Uncontrolled quivering around the lips

Tensing of the neck and shoulder muscles reducing the flow of saliva to the throat leading to dryness of the throat and vocal cords – quivering voice

Accelerated heart rate and increased blood pressure

Digestive movements cause feelings of nausea or possible vomiting

Shallow and rapid breathing

Increased production of adrenalin, noradrenalin, cortisone, endorphins and other hormones and raised blood glucose levels

Tensed and contracted muscles of the trunk and limbs; this may cause uncontrolled movement or shaking in knees, arms and finger tips

PHYSICAL EFFECTS

What happens to my body to produce such a response?

- The muscles become slightly tensed and ready to move so we can move quickly should there be any danger. *This causes the feelings of tension in the muscles.*
- Oxygen reacts with glucose producing lactic acid in the muscles as they need and demand more energy.
- The heart has to beat stronger for more oxygen to be taken through the bloodstream to the muscles, *which results in palpitations.*
- To get more oxygen into the blood system, the lungs have to work harder to take in more air. *This is why breathing becomes faster and shallow.*
- Blood is diverted away from those organs not needed to protect the body. For example blood is directed to muscles and away from the digestive system. *This causes the feeling of nausea and dizziness.*
- When muscles have to tense, they work harder, heightening the danger of the body overheating. *Sweating and flushing is the body's way of getting rid of this extra heat.*
- The body tries to become lighter which *results in an urge to pass urine or empty the bowels.*
- In order to keep this whole reaction going over a period of time, the hormone adrenalin is needed. This is pumped into the blood stream by the adrenal glands.

Exercise task 3

What does this response mean to you physically?

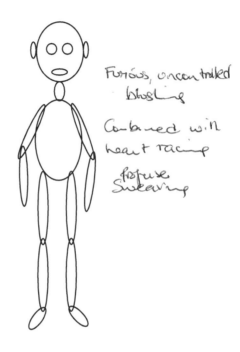

Furious, uncontrolled
blushing

Combined with
heart racing

profuse
Sweating

Personal Diagram

Description of a panic attack

Panic attacks may result from a build up of stress. The symptoms of panic often cause a person to become so attentive to bodily sensations such as a tight chest or dizziness, that the symptoms become more of a problem than the original stressor.

The person becomes so attuned to their body sensations that it activates the alarm when no danger is present – this is the over sensitive activation of the fight / flight alarm. Something similar to a smoke alarm sounding at the slightest trigger! The result is that a vicious circle is created.

A person starts to scan the environment for possible anxiety cues, there is a focusing inwards on bodily reactions such as sweating or dizziness, along with the catastrophic misinterpretation; thoughts of 'I'm having a heart attack', or 'I'm going crazy,' with the desire to escape; take flight.

For example a sudden onset of intense apprehension/fear may be experienced as:

BODILY RESPONSE: palpitations, dizziness, chest pain, shaking etc.

With;

THOUGHTS: 'I'm going to have a heart attack,' 'I'm going to lose control'

With;

BEHAVIOUR: People often try to escape the situation quickly. This avoidance brings temporary relief, but increases the likelihood of future apprehension and fear, negative thoughts, and bodily symptoms. This increases the desire to scan for possible anxiety cues in the environment and for selective attention to bodily sensations. This cycle results in the person seemingly having no obvious external reason for the panic attacks, they appear unpredictable. They experience intense discomfort and the need to escape. These symptoms can be very distressing.

IT IS IMPORTANT TO REMEMBER that these feelings themselves, though unpleasant, are not harmful and do not indicate that there is something seriously wrong with you.

How anxiety and panic are maintained by our behaviour

Over sensitivity

As already discussed these factors influence the development of panic attacks and also help to maintain the cycle of anxiety and panic disorder. It is understandable that as people start to realize that their symptoms mean physical or mental discomfort they start to scan for possible cues, however this oversensitivity can lead to misinterpretation of cues.

Avoidance

People often avoid situations where panic attacks occur or activities that may trigger symptoms associated with panic.

Avoidance would seem to make sense in terms of self-protection, to avoid the physical discomfort of difficult situations.

While avoidance reduces the symptoms in the short term, it also reduces the opportunity to learn that anxiety symptoms, while uncomfortable are not dangerous.

Avoidance prevents a person from 'disconfirming' their FEARS. The more we don't do something, go shopping for example, the more we tell ourselves we can't do it.

Avoidance leads to loss of independence and confidence and will in time affect relationships.

Safety Behaviours

Safety behaviours are triggered when we don't completely avoid a situation where we think panic attacks may happen. Instead we go into the situation and behave in ways that will minimise the anxiety symptoms. These may be termed 'subtle avoidance' and result in you never losing the fear of your panic attack. This means you maintain the worry about the fears.

Examples of safety behaviour

- Keeping an eye on an escape route and not getting fully involved.
- Trying to amuse people and telling jokes.
- Letting your hair fall in front of your face; wearing clothes that hide parts of your body.
- Holding things tightly, locking your knees together to control shaking.

- Hiding your hands or your face; putting your hands to your face.
- Speaking slowly, or quietly; or talking fast and not taking time to draw breath.
- Rehearsing what you are about to say; mentally checking that you have got your words right.
- Putting things off such as meeting friends; not shopping at busy time.
- Keeping safe: choosing safe places; or talking to safe people about safe topics.
- Always agreeing with people; not expressing a personal opinion.
- Wanting to hide; making yourself inconspicuous at social events.
- Avoiding eye contact with other people.
- Sitting at the back of a room or restaurant.

Subtle kinds of safety behaviours

- Seeking reassurance: The person constantly seeks reassurance to boost their confidence. This shows that the person subconsciously has doubts that they or the situation will be ok. This constant seeking of reassurance maintains the anxiety cycle because they never discover that they are and will be ok in the feared situation and so confidence is eroded.
- Dependence: A kind friend or relative's helpful behaviour; although from a generous motive can contribute to maintaining the anxiety cycle. For example, a friend getting someone's shopping when

they are anxious to go in the shop themselves. Partners being over protective of one another.

- Waiting for someone else to arrive before entering a room full of people.
- Being busy; by handing things around at a party rather than stopping to talk; staying in the kitchen at a social event to avoid getting into a conversation with someone.
- Not using public toilets when you know others are using them.
- Avoiding talking about anything personal.
- Not eating in public places.
- Turning away or hiding when you see someone you know approaching.
- Looking at the floor so that no one gives you eye contact.
- Wearing heavy make up to hide blushing.
- Leaving a room immediately after a meeting to avoid getting involved in small talk.

Exercise task 4

Identifying my avoidance and safety behaviour

The things I avoid or have stopped doing because of my anxiety / panic:

1. Staying for coffee after church
2. Contacting friends to arrange meeting
3.

4...
5...

Things that I do to make myself feel safer when anxious / panic:

1...... hibernate ....
2...... go quiet ....
3...
4...
5...

How to handle panic attacks

It is important to remember that once the physical symptoms have been diagnosed by a health professional as panic attacks, though uncomfortable, they will not harm you. The panic attacks, once triggered, affect our thinking process, our physiology and our behaviour. It can also affect our relationship with God! As with anxiety it is important to start to monitor your panic attacks in order to understand them and in order to inform a health professional.

Exercise task 5

Keep a diary to monitor panic attacks

This may include:

Date and time of day the panic attack occurred.

....

Was your panic attack expected?

Yes   No

The situation; where were you? What were you doing?

....
....
....

What were you thinking / predicting when you began to feel anxious (thoughts in words or images)?

....
....
....

What were you feeling (e.g. anxious, panicky, afraid etc.)?

....
....
....

What did you do to stop your predictions from coming true – avoidance and or safety behaviours?

....
....
....

What were your prominent physical symptoms?

....
....
....

Where was Jesus? Did you ask Him for help? (Remember the disciples' in the storm.)

....
....
....

How we breathe in anxiety and panic attacks

When we are anxious or in a state of panic our breathing can be significantly disrupted. When we breathe in we take in oxygen that is used by the body then breathe out carbon dioxide. There has to be a balance between the two and this balance is maintained by how fast and deeply we breathe.

When we are anxious this balance is disrupted and we begin to over-breathe, or hyperventilate. We all hyperventilate when we are tense or anxious or doing exercise. We breathe faster in order to provide our muscles with the oxygen to burn during activity. In this way the body is prepared for action to relieve stress and anxiety by fighting or running. However, when over-breathing becomes a habit, it becomes a problem. Continuous over-breathing causes oxygen levels in the blood to rise too much and at the same time the carbon dioxide levels fall, which causes unpleasant physical symptoms such as dizziness or light headedness.

Some people with panic attacks may over-breathe producing these symptoms. This can be distressing and can be misinterpreted catastrophically as a heart attack.

It is important to start to recognise the symptoms of over-breathing; breathing too fast. It is necessary to learn to relax and be calm rather than tense with raised shoulders.

Exercise task 6

Square breathing

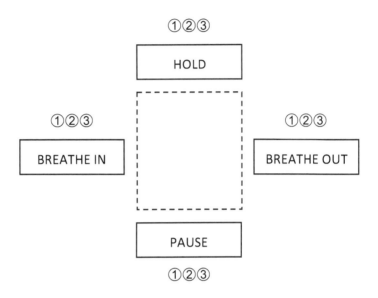

- With your eyes closed try to imagine a square in your mind.
- Imagine walking up the left side of the square, as you do breathe in for a count of 3.
- As you imagine you are walking across the top of the square, hold your breath for the count of 3.
- As you imagine walking down the right side of the square, you breathe out for 3.
- As you imagine walking across the bottom of the square you hold for the count of 3.
- Then start again.

- These are normal breaths not deep breaths.

Re-breathing: This method can be used if you do not catch the hyperventilation in time. You will be breathing in the air you have just breathed out by placing your cupped hands over your nose and mouth. Breathe in through your nose and out through your mouth. Breathe in your own exhaled air. Repeat slowly 4 or 5 times.

Relaxation Skills

As discussed, stress responses are controlled by the autonomic nervous system in combination with stress hormones, particularly adrenalin. Although this response is automatic there are things we can do to help!

The arousal system (sympathetic) is responsible for the 'fight / flight' response to stress.

The 'relaxation' system (Parasympathetic) is responsible for helping us to sleep, digest our food and rest.

If we learn to switch on the 'relaxation' system the 'arousal' system will have to switch off. They cannot both operate at the same time.

Relaxation is helpful when dealing with anxiety and panic because when stressed, the muscles in our bodies tense up and this muscular tension causes additional discomfort, for example headaches or pain across the shoulders, etc.

This additional tension can increase worry, making people even more anxious, tense and tired. This creates a further vicious cycle.

Relaxing in response to this tension is an effective way to control the tension as it slows down the bodily systems that speed up when we are anxious.

When we learn how to relax we can help relieve the symptoms of tension. It is impossible to feel tension and relaxation at the same time.

Relaxation is a skill to be learned.

Remember though:

- Plan in advance times when you will practice relaxation and try to set a routine.
- Make sure you are somewhere quiet, where no one will disturb you.
- If you experience worrying intruding thoughts don't focus on them. Let them go and focus your mind on positives.
- Check the environment is relaxing and quiet.
- It takes time and practice and discipline to relax.

Relaxation may include:

A warm bath, listening to music, or coffee with friends; relaxation may also take the form of a more practiced exercise as follows:

Tensing and relaxing exercise

- Lie on the floor or sit comfortably in a chair with feet slight apart, eyes closed or looking down. Feel the floor or chair take your weight and let your mind rid itself of intrusive thoughts. Be aware of your breathing, deeply and slowly.
- Now you are going to tense and relax your muscles. Tense all the muscles in your body, feel the tension, hold the muscles as tight as you can, concentrate on the feeling. Now let go – relax; let the tension gradually ease away. Notice the difference of feeling relaxed. Repeat one more time – tense; relax.
- Focusing on your feet: point your toes, stretch your feet. Hold for 7 seconds and let go. Repeat. Gently shake your feet.
- Focusing on your legs; stretch your legs one at a time as straight as possible pulling your toes back as you stretch your leg. Hold for 7 seconds and let go.
- Focusing on your bottom; clench the muscles of your buttocks for 7 seconds, hold and then let go. Repeat.
- Stomach; pull your stomach muscles in as hard as you can, hold for 7 seconds and let go. Repeat.
- Back; only if you are able, arch your back and hold for 7 seconds and let go. Repeat.
- Focus on your hands. Squeeze them tightly into a fist; clench them tighter and tighter still. Be aware of the tension in your hands. Hold for 7 seconds. Then let the tension go and relax your fingers for about 10 seconds. Repeat.
- Now flex your elbows, tensing your arms and forcing your right knuckle into your right shoulder and your

left knuckle into your left shoulder. Keep this position of tension for 7 seconds, then let go and let your arms go floppy, give them a shake, relax. Repeat.

- Now for your shoulders; pull your shoulders up to your ears. Tense them tightly, hold and let go. Repeat. Shake your arms and feel the tension go. Focus on your neck; push your chin into your chest and hold for 7 seconds. Hold and let go. Repeat.
- Focus on your face and screw your face up as hard as you can, hold for 7 seconds and let go. Repeat.
- Focusing on your scalp open your eyes as wide as possible and hold for 7 seconds and let go. Repeat.
- When you have completed the exercise you may be aware of parts of the body that are still tense, repeat the appropriate section of the exercise for those parts.

Physical exercise

Physical exercise is another way to deal with the physical effects of anxiety. Jogging, walking, cycling or gardening can help reduce muscle tension within the body.

When panic occurs

Remember panic symptoms are not harmful and nothing worse will happen.

1. Panic is an exaggerated normal reaction to perceived danger.

2. Be aware of what is happening to your body. Stay with the present.
3. Negative thinking about what may happen is not helpful.
4. Try to stay calm as the symptoms will peak and begin to subside.
5. Monitor your level of anxiety. 10 (being worst) to 0 (being least). Notice your anxiety level reducing.
6. Stay in the situation. If you avoid it, it will be more fearful in the future.
7. Take some slow deep breaths.
8. Relax the tense muscles.
9. Ask Jesus into your panic / storm.

Begin to concentrate on your previous activity.

HOME ACTIVITY

Task 1

Take time to practice the Square breathing technique when you are not feeling anxious or having a panic attack. This will enable you to apply the technique with greater ease when you are anxious or having a panic attack.

Task 2

Try to build relaxation time into your daily life.

Task 3

Remember to focus on God's love for you!

Summary Module 2

ϟ Our response to anxiety and panic is significantly affected by the truth of who we are in relation to God.

ϟ Faced with anxiety and panic, our reaction is to fight, to take flight or indeed to freeze.

ϟ Helpful breathing and relaxation techniques and knowing the foundations of God's love for us help us to combat the anxiety and panic symptoms.

Module 3

The role of behaviour in the anxiety response

"Worrying is like a rocking chair, it gives you something to do, but it gets you nowhere."

- Glen Turner

Introduction 77

Dealing with avoidance and safety
behaviours 77

The anxiety curve 82

Dealing with the root of fear 86

Things to consider while handling
avoidance 89

Distraction 94

Home activity 100

Summary of module 3 101

Introduction

This module will continue to focus on the role of behaviour in anxiety. It will particularly discuss how anxiety is reduced by facing our fears rather than maintained by using avoidance and safety behaviours, which help maintain our fears by creating a vicious circle of anxiety symptoms.

The module will describe how to deal with avoidance using graded exposure exercises and distraction strategies. These strategies are to be encouraged whilst focusing on who we are in God. We will also re-visit the breathing techniques discussed in the previous module.

Dealing with avoidance and safety behaviours

As already mentioned people avoid or withdraw from situations in which they have previously become anxious due to fear and so participate less in everyday activities, for example going shopping or going into crowded places.

Avoidance is not doing something because to do it would make you feel anxious. Avoidance makes sense in terms of self-protection, however though it may be one way of reducing anxiety in the short term it plays a key part in establishing and maintaining the anxiety cycle, as we never learn to 'disconfirm' our fears.

Safety behaviours develop because people with anxiety focus on how to keep themselves safe and do a wide variety of things to reduce the sense of risk they face, for example, by asking other people to do the shopping. Safety behaviours decrease our confidence over time because they leave you with the message that you need protecting, that you will be unsafe without them. They give you the illusion that they work, that the threat has been prevented. (See module two to review examples of avoidance and safety behaviours).

It is important to state here that Father God does not want his children to live in fear. It is difficult for Christians when suffering from anxiety and panic to be told 'stop being anxious, trust in God'!

For example, when the disciples were in the boat and the storm was raging and fear overtook them; it's hard to not be anxious when you are terrified and feel that you are about to drown!

The reality is all Christians struggle in different ways and all are on a journey of deepening trust and faith in a relationship with a living God. There is enough guilt from being anxious without more being piled higher through the 'you should' and 'ought to' of others.

However, there is a need to take a stand, draw a line and recognise that anxiety is fear based and it is a spiritual battle. A choice needs to be made to face the fear in order to take hold of life and live it in all its fullness. It is recognising that our own "cisterns", systems or strategies to survive fail us and that all are on a journey to learn more of who God is and what it means to trust him in our storm and for him to deliver each one from fear.

Psalm 34:4 says:

I sought the Lord, and he answered me;

He delivered me from all my fears.

Those who look to him are radiant;

Their faces are never covered with shame.

This poor man called, and the Lord heard him;

He saved him from all his troubles.

The angel of the lord encamps around those who fear him, and he delivers them.

It is a prayerful journey to be taken and we need to recognise that 'delivered from all my fears' does not equate to using avoidance! Sadly, many Christians fall into the avoidance trap and assume they are walking by faith.

Does Jesus understand anxiety, was he ever so distressed? Read afresh Luke 22:44. (Jesus 'anguish of soul' is foretold in Isaiah 53)

"And being in anguish, he prayed more earnestly, and his sweat was like drops of blood falling to the ground"...

Remember while Jesus was fully God, he was fully man. Jesus did not use His divinity to avoid any pain. He felt it all in his physical body and knowing what was ahead experienced extreme anguish in his mind and emotions. This was the cost for Jesus in showing his love for mankind. He asked three times to avoid the imminent trial he was to endure. He, more than anyone, understands the desire to avoid a fearful situation due to anxiety!

Sweating drops of blood is a rare medical condition; hematohidrosis – here the blood vessels constrict due to extreme stress and then dilate to the point of rupture, so releasing blood into the sweat glands.

Jesus as a human being suffered. The 'cup 'in the Garden of Gethsemane is a reflection of his inner torment, anxiety, loss, fear and low mood.

As with Jesus who prayed to his father, prayer is for us a key weapon in confronting disturbed emotions! It is a journey.

Exercise task 1

1. List the problems created when using avoidance and safety behaviours.

   ....
   ....
   ....

2. How do they restrict your life?

   ....
   ....
   ....

3. Identify a situation you have avoided recently.

   ....
   ....
   ....

4. Describe the thoughts / images you had and why you decided to avoid the situation?

   ....
   ....
   ....

5. What do you think would have happened if you had stayed in the situation would your anxiety have increased, decreased or stayed the same?

   ....
   ....
   ....

6. Identify a particular safety behaviour, which you use and think about how this may be unhelpful?

   ....
   ....
   ....

7. What long-term effect could safety behaviour or avoidance have on you?

....

....

....

8. How does using these self-protective behaviours hinder your trust in God?

....

....

....

9. Start to pray about the fear behind why you avoid situations and why you use safety behaviours.

....

....

....

The Anxiety Curve

The anxiety curve helps us to see what happens to our behaviour in relation to anxiety. When considering what would happen in a feared situation, would your anxiety increase, decrease or stay the same? Most anxious people would say, "increase". They fear the worst will happen: they may faint or have a heart attack. On the graph they imagine the line going up and up and off the page.

However, this belief is not true. Experiments and experience with anxious people has shown that the anxiety will peak and then decrease of its own accord. This means that the more an anxious person faces the fear, the more the initial anxiety will decrease, as does the duration time of the anxiety.

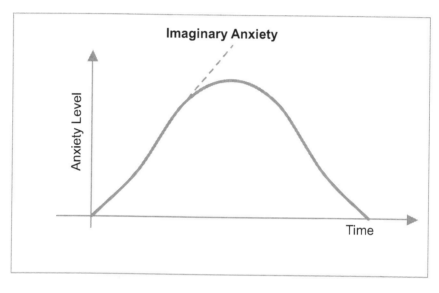

ANXIETY CURVE AND AVOIDANCE

Each time we successfully avoid the situation and our anxiety, we make it more likely that the next time the feared situation crops up we will avoid it again.

If you leave the situation quickly, you will never find out.

As an anxious person exposes himself or herself to the feared situation repeatedly taking small steps to manage their anxiety, the person's anxiety reduces over time. *If you leave the situation quickly rather than tolerate the anxiety you will never find this out!*

Each time we put ourselves in a fearful situation our anxiety will initially increase, but will then reach a plateau, and then decrease. The first time you remain in a situation the anxiety takes time to subside. The second time the anxiety will be less severe and will reduce more quickly. The diagram shows that anxiety, which is experienced over time, will reduce as it is faced rather than avoided.

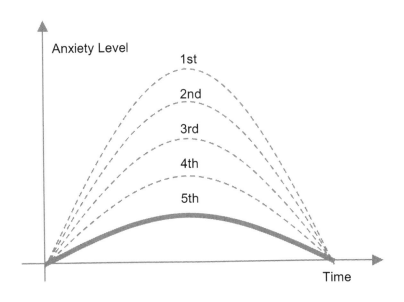

Now that we understand what is happening when we feel anxious, the next step is to overcome the avoidance pattern. It is important that we continue to draw near to God so that he can draw near to us and to continue to resist walking away from our fears and anxiety symptoms.

Exercise task 2

Prayerfully ask God to help you make a list of all the situations or activities you have been avoiding. List the situations or activities from the most difficult to those that are difficult but most do-able. (See example of case study on p.88)

MOST DIFFICULT

1 5

2 4

3 3

4 2

5 1

MOST DO-ABLE

Now taking the easiest activity, the most do-able; or situation it is important to identify your **fear!**

1.   What is it exactly that makes you anxious?

....

....

....

2.   What is the worst that can happen to you?

....

....

....

3.   What makes it easier or more difficult: e.g., is it a particular shop, the time of day, the number of people?

....

....

....

Dealing with the root of fear

It is important to prayerfully involve God: imagine anxiety to be a plant above the soil's surface but the root under the soil is called FEAR.

Start to ask God to show you when the root of 'fear' got access into your life.

Key questions may be:

- When did it start?

- What was happening practically?

- Why did it start?

- Who was with you?

- What was being said?

As you ask these questions ask the Holy Spirit to direct you. It is helpful as you take these steps in the journey away from fear and anxiety to have someone pray with you and for you. As a response you may be led to acts of:

Repentance: (2 Corinthians 7:10) Being regretful, sorrowful about how you have lived in fear and resolve not to continue living in fear and trusting in things other than God to protect you, such as using avoidance or safety behaviours. (1 John 1:9)

Forgiveness: (Matthew 6:12) Forgiving, pardoning those who may have caused you personal hurt. This may be a journey for some when there has been deep and significant hurt, particularly if the fear and anxiety is as a consequence of childhood trauma or abuse

There may be a need to personally ask for forgiveness from others if your behaviours have caused hurt to others.

Healing and comfort: (Acts 10:38, Luke 9:11) Asking the Holy Spirit to come into those painful memories to bring healing and restoration (Read Isaiah 61)

Delivered from all our fears: (Psalm 34) asking God to fill us to overflowing with his love that drives out all fear (Ephesians 3:18).

As you have prayed it is important to put into action new behaviours to break the habits of the old fear driven ones. Some may be able to go straight to the activity they had avoided after praying. Others may need to take small achievable steps to enable achievement of the task. The key is that you don't let fear rule your life!

CASE STUDY

Ms Apricot who is anxious about driving her car after being in a car accident will take time to pray using the following model: Repentance, forgiveness or forgiving, receiving healing, being delivered from fear and anxiety, being filled with the Holy Spirit and Gods love.

She may then create the following task 'ladder' programme starting at the lowest rung and working up to the top until the goal is reached so enabling her to build her confidence in driving again.

The goal is: to drive her daughter to school in the car.

Fear stated as: 'I'm going to get hurt. I will never be able to drive again'

List the situations or activities:

8. Drive with daughter in car when school run time.   (*Most difficult*)

7. Drive alone when school run time

6. Drive with a friend when school run time.

5. Drive to school with a friend when not school run time.

4. Drive around the block with a friend.

3. Drive to the end of the road with a friend.

2. Sit in the car and start it up.

1. Sit in the car with a friend.   (*Most do-able*)

Tasks on ladder!

Starting from the bottom the person practices each feared situation until their anxiety is reduced.

Things to consider while handling avoidance

1. Set the goals you want to achieve

2. State what the named fear is and take time to talk to God and ask God to set you free from it.

3. Ask someone to pray with you.

4. Rank your tasks in order of difficulty starting with the easiest, most do-able first at the base of the ladder.

5. Plan a series of small specific tasks.

6. The difficulty should increase slowly in order to reach your end goal.

7. The task can develop in various ways; you may want to imagine yourself doing it first. It is important to only alter one aspect of your task each time.

8. Practise the task regularly – you may need to do it several times in one day.

9. It is helpful to note your anxiety rating so you can observe the improvement! *Anxiety level at start of task 0-10*

10. Do not move on to the next task until your anxiety has reduced.

11. Praise yourself as you recognise your achievements.

12. Praise God for setting you free from fear!

You may experience setbacks along the route to recovery, but don't despair. These can be a common feature of recovery.

If you find fear starting to return; be kind to yourself and review the strategy first used for getting free from fear. The key is to identify if something has provoked the fear. Also ask someone to pray with you. Remember Satan, the 'accuser,' wants you to remain fearful.

Exercise task 3 – RECORD SHEET

My goal is to:

....

....

....

What I fear is: Rate 0 – 10 (10 being the worst)

....

....

....

Which fear am I asking God to help me with?

....

....

....

Who am I going to ask to pray with me?

....

....

....

What do I need to repent of?

....

....

....

Who do I need to forgive?

....

....

....

Who do I need to ask to forgive me or make restitution with?

....

....

....

Did I receive prayer for healing and comfort?

....

....

....

Did I receive prayer to be delivered from the root of fear and anxiety?

....

....

....

Ask someone to pray with you that you may receive a new understanding of God's love that 'casts out fear' and of the truth of Ephesians 3 where we read of the depth, breadth, height and width of God's marvellous love. Pray that the Holy Spirit would come and heal and fill you anew.

Tasks to achieve my goal

(Commencing with easiest task advancing to most difficult to achieve the goal)

7..

6..

5..

4..

3..

2..

1..

- Anxiety level at start of task 0-10

- Anxiety level at end of task 0-10

- What have I learned?

- How am I going to praise God and be kind to myself?

Distraction

A definition of distraction: is something that diverts the mind, interruption, amusement, or relaxation from work. Anxiety symptoms are unpleasant particularly as a person battles with irrational thoughts. Distraction can be an effective way to cope with the increasing vicious spiral of anxiety symptoms. The distraction serves to interrupt the thoughts breaking the hard work of negative thinking. It enables us to stay in the anxiety-provoking situation, thus not avoiding, whilst helping the mind to refocus.

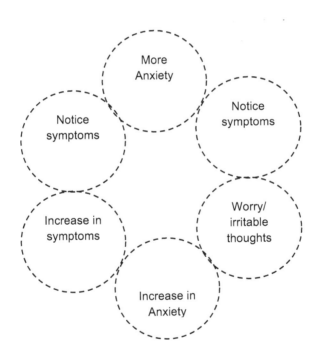

The aim is to turn our attention from the negative thoughts and anxiety symptoms by engaging in activities that will distract our attention thus breaking the cycle.

This may be done by considering using:

1. *The traffic light game;* as soon as you start thinking negative statements about yourself ('I cannot do this', 'I am a failure'), say to yourself:

   'Halt!! Danger! The Red traffic light is on.'
   Mentally picture the red traffic light and say to yourself I am not going down this road!!

2. *Make a point of thinking a positive thought about yourself and move down a new road!* You might want to carry 'Truth cue cards' with self-praise statements on. This is a small piece of card with a positive self-praise statement written on it.

> ### TRUTH CUE CARD
>
> # STOP!
>
> I MAY FEEL ANXIOUS BUT THESE
> SYMPTOMS CANNOT HARM ME. THE
> SYMPTOMS WILL PASS. I CAN DO THIS.
>
> ## RELAX!

3. *You may engage in the Biblical approach* to distraction by fixing or setting your mind upon the truth of how God perceives you.

I am accepted: *I am no longer rejected or unloved. In Christ I am completely accepted.*

God says:

John 1:12 – I am God's child.

John 15:15 – As a disciple, I am a friend of Jesus Christ.

Ephesians 1: 3-8 – I have been chosen by God and adopted as his child.

1 Corinthians 6: 19 – I have been bought with a price. I belong to God.

I am secure: *I am no longer unprotected, alone or abandoned. In Christ I am secure.*

God says:

Romans 8: 31-39 - I cannot be separated from the love of God.

2 Timothy 1:7 – I have not been given a spirit of fear but of power, love and a sound mind.

I am significant: *I am no longer worthless, inadequate or hopeless. In Christ I am deeply significant and special.*

God says:

Ephesians 2:10 – I am God's workmanship.

Ephesians 3:12 – I may approach God with freedom and confidence.

Ephesians 2:6 – I am seated with Christ in the heavenly realms.

It may help to have 'Truth' cards - that is to carry small cards in your pocket with Bible verses on.

4. *It is helpful to have worship songs that are personally appropriate to your situation and that you can sing to yourself.*

5. *Bible meditation* enables you to focus your mind on key passages about who God is and what He can do.

6. *Playing mental games that engage the mind* such as reciting poetry, mind puzzles such as counting backwards from a hundred in fives and then threes.

7. *Trying to focus on the environment you are in.* For example be aware of the buildings, or types of cars. Start to describe something in detail.

8. *Using a bridging object;* a small object in your pocket that reminds you of a happy occasion and generates positive memories.

9. *Physical activity;* this particularly helps get rid of the extra adrenalin and will help your body to be less tense.

10. *Relaxation;* helps your body relax and serves as a distraction as you focus on your breathing and becoming calm.

Exercise task 4

Think of two distraction strategies that you may already use that are helpful and consider two more you would like to consider trying over the next week.

Two strategies I already use to help distract me:

1	
2	

Two additional strategies I may try:

1	
2	

These distraction strategies can be employed as you engage in the handling avoidance exercise.

Exercise task 5

You may want to keep a diary of the distraction strategies employed in relation to the avoidance step-by-step ladder in order to monitor which distractions are helpful.

Date	
Goal to be challenged	
Anxiety before (0-10)	
Anxiety after (0-10)	
Distraction used during tasks	
Outcome: Was the distraction helpful or unhelpful	

HOME ACTIVITY

Task 1

At this stage it would be helpful to start to apply modules 1, 2 and 3 into your daily living activities and life style.

Try to practise and use the Square breathing, relaxation and distraction techniques.

Be increasingly aware of what you are avoiding or the safety behaviours you are using.

Remember this is a journey and it takes time!

Task 2

Make a goal of talking to someone about the 'root of fear' that was discussed in the module and ask him or her to pray with you.

Remember God is for you!

Summary of module 3

§ We now have an understanding of anxiety and panic and how they are established and maintained.

§ We have considered breathing, relaxation, a gradual graded exposure approach and distraction as strategies to help manage our anxiety symptoms.

Module 4

Understanding How Thinking Affects Anxiety

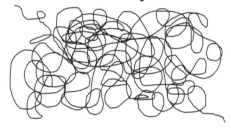

"Worry is a complete cycle of inefficient thought revolving about a pivot of fear."

- Anonymous

Introduction   105

The power of thoughts   105

Understanding Self talk   108

What are thoughts?   109

Thoughts and feelings   111

Anxiety and negative automatic thoughts   112

Negative thinking styles   117

Home Activity   123

Summary   126

Introduction

This module will particularly focus on self-evaluation – the journey of discovering how personal negative thoughts affect anxiety.

The power of thoughts

Few people give much attention to their 'thought life' (what they are thinking), compared to their outward life. Consider how much more attention is given to daily clothing choices as compared to knowing what we are currently thinking at any given moment!

Henry David Thoreau said, *"Thought is the sculptor who can create the person you want to be."*

God certainly wants us to be equipped for the emotional, spiritual, intellectual and mind warfare that we face daily as believers. To win any battle, a soldier, along with his team, must use strategies to defend his base from the attack of the enemy. As we have seen in the previous modules, our minds process thoughts and feelings with resulting behavioural actions. It is true that an individual's thought life can cause great suffering. We have the choice in life to accept conditions as they exist, or accept the responsibility for changing the conditions. Our mind is a key component.

It is important not to underestimate the degree to which the thoughts you accept as truth impact the emotions, or underestimate the words and the actions that create the world you live in.

It is important for a person to keep his thoughts concentrated on good things and to abstain from dwelling on negative thoughts! As Philippians 4:8 says, 'whatever is just, whatever is pure, whatever is lovely, whatever is gracious, if there is any excellence, if there is anything worthy of praise, think about these things.' The scriptures hold the strategies for a healthy mind!

Samuel Smiles wrote:

> *Sow a thought and you reap an act,*
> *Sow an act and you reap a habit,*
> *Sow a habit and you reap a character,*
> *Sow a character and you reap a destiny!*

The thoughts we have play a significant role in increasing or decreasing our emotional health and therefore, anxiety. People can struggle with intrusive or automatic thoughts and with dysfunctional beliefs and attitudes. These automatic thoughts can provoke immediate emotional reactions that can lead to longer-term habits.

Our thought life, if left untamed, can result in negative attitudes and habits of thinking that can lead to distress and will have resulting behavioural consequences.

Our own thoughts can produce wellness or they can produce pain; discouragement, fears, self-doubt and negativity. Our thought life therefore plays a major role in the way we handle life and circumstances.

As Christians it is necessary to understand that 'We have the mind of Christ.' *(1 Corinthians 2:16)* Author Bill Johnson, suggests, God has made our minds to be the Gatekeeper of Kingdom of God activity. The mind is the essential tool in bringing Godly reality to the problems and crises people face on a daily basis. Only a renewed mind can bring emotional health. Renewing of the mind begins with repentance, which enables a return to God's perspective on reality. The Bible informs us in Romans 8:6 that the mind controlled by the Spirit is life and peace.

Thought life can be like the complex workings of a computer. As a computer may be infected by a virus and so produce bizarre activity and eventually instability, loss of data and ultimate breakdown, so it is with the mind. Once it is set on a habit of negative thoughts it has commenced a self-destructive mode which will ultimately lead to fear, anxiety, self harming behaviours and lack of well-being.

It is therefore vital that we learn to be aware of what we are thinking and learn to focus our thoughts on things that are right, pure, lovely, admirable, excellent, and praise worthy. *(Philippians 4:8)* This module will focus on identifying those negative thinking styles in order that in the next module we can learn how to challenge and handle negative thinking.

Research suggests that many people who suffer from anxiety make matters worse for themselves by misinterpreting their physical symptoms. For example, 'I'm going to have a heart attack,' 'I'm going to embarrass myself,' 'I'm going to be out of control.' These thoughts cause fear and help to maintain the anxiety. They are indeed distortions of what is actually happening.

Sometimes we are unaware of these thoughts because they occur so quickly and automatically. It is important, indeed necessary to identify these thoughts and recognize the role they play in creating and maintaining anxiety. It is important to recognise that our imaginations can create either a work of art that is beautiful or turn it into a horror movie. When our thought life is consistently negative it can be like living in a horror movie.

It is at this point that one can take hold of the truth that God **IS** mindful of us *(Psalm 8:4, Luke 1:48, Hebrews 2:6)*; that the Bible teaches us how to guard our minds. *(Philippians 4:8, 1 Peter 5:7)*

Understanding Self-talk

We all talk to ourselves. This is what makes up a large part of our thinking! If our Self-talk is too negative it can result in worrying thoughts and loss of confidence.

Unhelpful Self-talk can be focused on how we perceive ourselves and /or how we imagine others perceive us. They can be rejection focused; self rejecting with self criticism and self judgement or rejection of others; which might include criticisms or judgements; 'They think I'm stupid,' 'I'll never be as good as my sister,' 'They are far more spiritual than me.' This can be hard to detect because with repetition the negative thoughts become habits and become so automatic we are not aware of them. These negative thinking habits are often in conflict with, and opposed to, the truth of how God perceives us.

What are thoughts?

The Concise Oxford dictionary defines *"Thought"* as a way of thinking characteristic of a person, or a process.

Thoughts can be likened to internal speech. However, people are often not aware of their thoughts and so do not consciously speak them out, or even seek them out. What a person thinks and the thoughts that go through their minds determine how they feel. For example when you are feeling good what sort of thoughts are going through your mind?

It is not an event or a situation that determines how a person feels emotionally, but the thoughts, meanings and interpretations the person brings to the situation or event. What you think, and the thoughts that go through your mind are what determine how you feel.

An event or circumstance prompts an internal appraisal; a thinking process occurs which leads to a feeling, an emotional response; this in turn results in a behavioural action.

It is we who decide how to judge, appraise, or interpret the event. It is this judgement, appraisal, or the interpretation of the circumstance, which determines whether we feel anxious or not. Thoughts then are likened to an internal speech where as feelings are an emotional process.

Here is an example of how an event can lead to different emotional and behavioural responses due to the internal thought appraisals:

A colleague has just been told he needs to attend a pub quiz:

Thought 1

I love pub quizzes, I know the type of questions they ask so it is ok!

Emotions: Happy
Behaviour: Check on the most recent Oscar awards.
Physical: Quite relaxed.

Thought 2

I'm hopeless at general knowledge. I will let my team down.

Emotions: anxious, fearful.
Behaviour: Arrives late, makes excuses.
Physical: Tense, tired.

Thought 3

Well I'm not good at general knowledge but it will be fun I will just go along.

Emotions: Neutral
Behaviour: Goes along, listens, has fun.
Physical: Quite relaxed.

When a negative thinking style is present, emotions like anxiety may result. The person may experience unpleasant physical symptoms and avoid doing a variety of activities.

It is important to learn to identify what we are thinking in any given situation in order to identify the negative thinking styles.

People often confuse thoughts and feelings. It is helpful to know the difference between them.

Thoughts and feelings

Thoughts: A way of thinking characteristic to a person. Often a thought is expressed as a sentence.

Emotions (Feelings): The affective state of consciousness in which joy, sorrow, fear, etc are present. A feeling is the emotional side of someone's character. A feeling is often expressed as one word.

Exercise task 1

Here is a list of thoughts and feelings. Go through the list and decide whether each item is a thought or a feeling.

Anger – It is all going well – I won't be able to do this – Frightened – A little sad – I feel stupid – Guilty – I don't know what to do – Happy – This is hopeless

THOUGHT	FEELING

Anxiety and negative automatic thoughts

When we feel anxious, tense or stressed our thinking tends to become more negative, irrational or unhelpful. We start to engage in negative and catastrophic thinking processes about events that may happen or things we predict could happen.

It is important to listen to your thoughts in order to identify the things you say to yourself. This may be difficult at first but with practise you will be able to easily notice the unhelpful things you say to yourself.

You may find you are jumping to conclusions, ignoring the positive things and only focusing on the negative, living through strict rules you have set yourself, *'I should be able' / 'I ought to'...*

Everyone has these negative automatic thoughts however people who do not complain of anxiety tend to balance their thoughts with more helpful, rational thoughts that counteract the negative.

Thoughts then, have a major role to play in maintaining anxiety. It is not the situation itself that causes the anxiety but a person's interpretation of the situation / event, in their thoughts, that causes the anxiety.

For example:

Event	Negative thought	Emotion
I am late for work	I will be cautioned	Fearful
Friend doesn't text	Does not care about me	Sad
I didn't get the job	I'm never going to get a job!	Hopeless

One way to lift negative emotions and unpleasant physical symptoms is to identify the negative thoughts that are unhelpful to you. Most people recognise a frightening thought in a particular situation. However, on a daily basis, we need to learn to recognise if a thought is helpful, life giving or unhelpful.

Exercise task 2

Read each thought about the event and decide whether you think it is helpful (H) or unhelpful (U) thinking. Please write "H" for helpful and "U" for unhelpful.

A colleague at work is having a birthday and you are asked to organise a collection for them.

I hate asking for money, I will blush.	
I will lose the money, or make a wrong choice of present.	
I will take someone along with me to help.	
They obviously trust me to do this!	
I am a little shy of asking for money but I can do this!	

Our thoughts and the ways in which we think can be unhelpful and results in feeling anxious and may lead to avoiding a situation.

OR

Thinking more helpful thoughts can result in feelings of hope and to behaving in a different way.

How we think therefore determines how we behave!

Exercise task 3

To help recognise the link between thoughts, feelings, physical response and behaviour, think about your personal reaction to a situation in which you recently found yourself that made you feel anxious.

Think about the situation that caused you anxiety.

....

....

....

Note the thoughts or image you had about it?

....

....

....

How did you respond emotionally?

....

....

....

What was the response physically?

....

....

....

How did this affect your behaviour?

....

....

....

How did it affect your response to God?

....

....

....

Was this helpful or unhelpful thinking?

....

....

....

Negative thinking styles

We are ALL prone at times to negative thinking styles, but when we are tired, under stress or anxious these styles become more exaggerated and influence our emotions and behavioural responses.

Exercise task 4

Read the common thinking styles below and see if you identify with any of them?

Negative thinking styles

Catastrophising: Anticipating disaster as the only outcome and not considering the alternatives. Thinking is dramatic and extreme.

All or nothing thinking: Seeing everything in all or nothing terms; sometimes called black and white thinking, expecting perfection in ourselves or others, this can set us up for further disappointment and distress.

Exaggerating: This involves magnifying negative or frightening experiences. We overestimate the chances of something happening or how bad it will be if it the experience does happen.

Over-generalising: Taking a single event and drawing much wider conclusions.

Filtering / ignoring the positives: Process of mentally filtering out the positive and reassuring facts and events. Not noticing compliments, acknowledging achievements or recognising one's strengths.

Scanning: Searching for the very thing we fear, which can lead to increased anxiety. It may increase the likelihood of seeing; feeling or hearing something frightening or it may mean you experience false alarms. This can trigger unjustified, but very real fear.

Mind reading: Thinking you know what others are thinking or how they are feeling (in general or about you), or thinking that you know their reason for acting as they do.

Personalisation: Thinking that everything others do or say is a reaction to you or says something about you, comparing yourself to other people.

Helplessness and responsibility (Control fallacies): seeing yourself as a helpless victim of fate, where everything is beyond your control and you underestimate what you can do to deal with the problem / situation (external control fallacy). Alternatively, you feel you are responsible for the pain or happiness of others around you (internal control fallacy).

Blaming: Holding others responsible for your pain. Alternatively you feel you are to blame for all your problems and other people's problems.

Emotional reasoning: Believing that what you feel must be true – I feel stupid means I am stupid! I feel a failure, so therefore I am a failure.

Should and ought to: your life rules about how you or others should act. Those who break the rules make you feel angry and you feel guilty, anxious or depressed if you break them.

Exercise task 5

From the example given below observe the negative thinking styles in relation to anxiety and how they can affect daily living:

A person goes into a doctor's practice and has to walk across the waiting room to get to the GP's consulting room:

"I'm starting to feel really anxious. My stomach doesn't feel good and I feel dizzy. I think I'm going to be sick! What happens if I'm sick, everyone will stare at me – I'll be too embarrassed to come back to see the GP ever again."

Negative thinking styles employed:

Catastrophising: Thinking that because they are anxious they will actually vomit and embarrass themselves.

Jumping to conclusions: when a person feels sick it does not mean they will be sick.

Exaggerating the importance of a situation: if the person was sick it would not mean they could never return to the GP practice again!

Exercise task 6

Negative thinking style quiz!

As you read the scenarios name the negative thinking styles in each statement.

Mary sees her friend Lucy walking along another shopping aisle. Mary thinks, "Lucy doesn't like me any more, she's ignoring me. I must have done something to upset her. I've never had many friends – I'm clearly not very likeable."

Negative thinking styles were:

- ....
- ....
- ....

Alice is in the dentist's and is kept waiting for her appointment. As she sits waiting she feels increasingly tense and angry. Alice thinks, "The dentist should be on time, we have to be on time! They just don't care about people like me. Just because they are professionals they think they are better than me. I'll be waiting for hours."

Negative thinking styles were:

- ....
- ....
- ....

Rachel overcooks the chicken while cooking a dinner for her partner's family. Rachel thinks, "Well the whole thing is spoiled now. I'm a dreadful cook and a complete failure at hospitality. I should have done better."

Negative thinking styles were:

- ....
- ....
- ....

Michael is about to give a lecture to his insurance colleagues and notices that he is feeling sick. Michael thinks 'what if I embarrass myself. What if I really am sick? I will make a real idiot of myself. This is going to be a nightmare.'

Negative thinking styles were:

- ....
- ....
- ....

It is evident that our negative thinking styles maintain the anxiety cycle. These styles eventually become a habit and with time become a stronghold – *a place dominated by particular characteristics of thought and behaviour.* As we begin to understand and identify these patterns of response we can begin to challenge them and replace the negative Self-talk or thoughts with positive thoughts.

For some these thinking styles have been in place unrecognized for many years. It is important however, to understand that God's love for you is not dependent on your thinking style. Ask Him to give you insight into your negative thinking and seek His help in the renewing of your mind. This process will take time, it is a 'Journey;' remember the *Recovery Curve diagram* at the beginning of the modules. It is important to learn to be kind to oneself as you pursue this new way of thinking.

HOME ACTIVITY

Task 1

Keep a thought record to help identify your thinking styles and how these affect emotional, physical and behavioural responses to your anxiety, including your relationship with God.

Date

....

What was the situation?

....
....
....

What thought or image did you have?

....
....
....

Can you identify your thinking style? For example: All or nothing thinking

....
....
....

What physical symptoms did you notice?

....
....
....

How did you feel emotionally?

....
....
....

What did you do? (Action taken)

....
....
....

Was your thinking helpful or unhelpful?

....
....
....

How did this affect your relationship with God?

....

....

....

Learning to abstain from negative thinking is a journey that takes time, with a need to recognise and identify the negative thoughts and then to have our minds renewed. It is a continuing prayer journey.

Task 2

Before commencing the next module look up the following Bible verses and use them as a basis for prayer:

- Renewing of the mind: Ephesians 4:22 and

  Romans 12: 2

- Peace of God: Philippians 4:4-7 and Isaiah 26:3

Summary of module 4

§ Thoughts play a significant role in increasing or
decreasing our anxiety.

§ The thought life, if left untamed, can result in negative
thinking and attitudes and habits of thinking that can
lead to distress. The result is emotional and
behavioural consequences that with time will affect
how we perceive ourselves and how we relate to God.

§ Thoughts have the capacity to produce wellness or
they can produce pain, discouragement, fears, self-
doubt or negativity! Thought life therefore plays a
major role in the way we handle life and
circumstances and it is therefore important that we
identify negative thinking styles in order to learn how
to challenge unhelpful thinking patterns.

Module 5

Challenging Unhelpful Thinking and Problem Solving

"Every thought is a seed. If you plant crab apples, don't count on harvesting Golden Delicious."

– Bill Meyer

Introduction   129

Is your thinking helpful or unhelpful?   129

3 steps to challenging thoughts   131

The importance of self-praise   137

Recovery of hope   139

Problem Solving   142

Summary   147

Introduction

The previous modules have established that anxiety does not come automatically from an event, but from our interpretation of an event. The appraisal or interpretation of an event will affect the way we feel emotionally and the consequential behaviour. The same event affects different people in different ways because each person has a different interpretation and therefore differing thoughts. Thoughts can be unhelpful or helpful. Unhelpful thoughts can be influenced by our negative thinking styles.

> *"Worry is a thin stream of fear trickling through the mind. If encouraged, it cuts a channel into which all other thoughts are drained".* Arthur Somers Roche

Is your thinking helpful or unhelpful?

Negative or unhelpful thinking can become so automatic (thoughts may come as images or half formed pictures in the mind) that the thought goes unnoticed and unchallenged, as though the thought was fact, leading a person to respond with anxiety.

'Here we go again, I'm stupid' with the physical response (heart racing, muscle tension), emotional response (fearful, anxious, worried, stressed) and behavioural (withdrawing, avoidance) anxiety responses. To break the vicious circle it is necessary to identify and challenge the anxious thought in order to find a more balanced helpful thought, which enables

129

positive Self-talk to commence. This is a process called *renewing the mind.*

"Drag your thoughts away from your troubles ... by the ears, by the heels, or by any other way you can manage it." Mark Twain

Exercise task 1

Identify Simon's helpful (H) and unhelpful (U) thinking in the following scenario. Please write "H" for helpful and "U" for unhelpful.

Simon has gone shopping. While in the shop he starts to feel anxious.

Everyone is looking at me.	
I'm going to throw up.	
I may be a little red and a few people may notice me.	
I'll just leave my shopping and get out of here quickly.	
I will stop a minute and practice the breathing exercises. Then I won't be sick and the feeling of panic will start to reduce.	

Which thoughts are more likely to lead to further anxiety symptoms?

3 Steps to Challenging Thoughts

As we become more aware of our thinking content we can then move on to identify, challenging and balancing the anxious thoughts.

Step 1: Identify the anxious thoughts

The best way to identifying anxious UNHELPFUL thoughts or images is to note them down when you are actually feeling the symptoms of anxiety. It is harder to remember them when you are calm.

Try asking yourself the following questions;

- 'What situation was I in?'
- 'What was I thinking (or what image did I see) just before I felt anxious?'
- 'Is this thought realistic?'
- 'What was I afraid would happen?'
- 'What was going through my mind?'
- 'What negative thinking style was I using?'

When we are anxious it is easy to avoid how we are thinking / feeling because it is uncomfortable.

It may be initially distressing to confront those thoughts and feelings and our anxiety may initially be heightened as we consider our thinking styles but be patient and persist as in the long term it will enable you to manage your anxiety symptoms.

Step 2: Challenge the anxious thoughts

Once you have identified the 'unhelpful' thought that maintains the anxiety it is important to find the 'helpful' thought that can help you feel less anxious and more able to manage the anxiety. This needs to be realistic and take account of all the information.

For example, if we consider *'People will think I am an idiot if I do...'* as a negative/unhelpful thought, we could challenge the thought by the following statements:

- Is there any evidence that people think I am an idiot?
- No one has ever said so. Feeling anxious cannot make me an idiot.
- I cannot read minds so how do I know what people may be thinking?
- Thinking like this does not help me.

Step 3: Balance the anxious thoughts

One way to learn to balance your negative, UNHELPFUL thought is to write two columns; one column for your thoughts that make you anxious and the other column for the balanced thought.

EXAMPLE

Anxious unhelpful thought	Balanced thought
What if I make a mistake?	Everyone makes mistakes.
I would embarrass myself.	I may learn how to cope with it.
I'm feeling dizzy. I will faint.	I have been dizzy many times and not fainted.
I might panic in front of everyone.	People are generally understanding and what is the worst that could happen

Referring back to the example in *Step 2,* a more balanced thought may be: *'I am not an idiot. We all make mistakes! I do not need to focus on what others think of me.'*

The following questions may help you to challenge your anxious (negative/ unhelpful) thought.

- What is the evidence for my negative thinking?
- Is there an alternative way of looking at my negative thinking?
- What is the worst that can happen?

- What is the best that can happen?
- What is the evidence against the thought?
- Is there an alternative explanation?
- What would my friends / family say to me?
- What would I say to my friend / family if they had this thought?
- Have I had experiences that show this thought not to be completely true?
- Am I using negative thinking styles, predicting the future, or trying to read other people's minds?
- Is this thought helpful or destructive?
- Is this thought helping or hindering me from achieving what I want?
- Am I discounting any positives?

Exercise task 2

Taking into account the 3 steps, consider a more realistic view of your anxious thought.

Step 1: Write down your anxious thought:

....

....

....

Step 2: Challenge the thought:

....

....

....

Step 3: A balanced thought may be:

....

....

....

Now review your unhelpful thought

Unhelpful thought   Balanced thought

....

....

....

....

It may feel like a battle initially to change from negative to positive thinking. Remember you may have created a habit of negative thought patterns. It can take time to renew our thinking. Truth cue cards may be a helpful prompter to help the renewing of thoughts.

Exercise task 3

TRUTH CUE CARDS

Once you have found a more balanced, realistic statement it may be helpful to write it down on a small card so that whenever you start to be negative in your thinking your 'truth' card will remind you of your balanced thought.

For example the TRUTH CUE CARD could have some of the following questions:

- What is the evidence for what I am thinking?

- Is this thought helpful or unhelpful?

- What would I say to a friend who was thinking this way?

- Does this help me to succeed?

- Is my thinking focusing on things that are good, pure, lovely, life giving?

The importance of self-praise

Self-talk is what we say to ourselves, which can help or hinder us in a situation. We can make Self-talk more positive by being 'active' in our thinking so it becomes Self-praise.

Self-praise breaks the vicious circle of the anxiety symptoms, whereas negative Self-talk leads to increased anxiety symptoms.

Self-praise helps us to **prepare** for a situation and **cope** with it. It is sometimes helpful to write some positive Self-talk statements down on a TRUTH CUE CARD.

Example

As you are preparing to go into a situation that has made you anxious in the past it is helpful to remind yourself:

1. *Preparation*

- If I do get anxious I know it's not helpful to avoid the situation.

- I might even enjoy the situation.

- It is better to go and see that I can cope.

- Each time I face my fears it gets easier.

- I will use my cue card questions to help me get a realistic view.

2. Coping

- I will remember my breathing techniques and relax.

- This is just anxiety, it will pass and I am not ill and I am not going to die.

- I know I am going to be ok, I know these symptoms. They will not defeat me.

- What are the positives I can focus on?

- Ask Jesus to be with you as He was with the disciples in the storm.

3. *Praise truth cards*

- I went into that situation and did well!

- I handled that and it will get easier next time.

- I am making definite progress!

- I'm proud of myself for facing that fear!

- Thank you God for helping me!

Have a go at creating your own statements that you can discreetly place on a small card that fits in a pocket or purse.

Recovery of Hope

The well-known Christian author, Corrie Ten Boom, said: "Any concern too small to be turned into a prayer is too small to be made into a burden."

The Bible tells us to 'cast our cares on God' (*1 Peter 5:7*); it is an encouragement to tell God all anxious thoughts.

Assurance through Jesus

The Bible speaks of the journey Jesus took with his disciples on the Road to Emmaus (*Luke 24:13*) when the disciples were confused, disillusioned and anxious. It tells of their journey of faith and how Jesus brought recovery of faith in three ways:

By being a good listener: he knew then and knows now that 'in God we sometimes doubt', he encouraged them to tell him what was happening in their lives. (*Luke 24:19*)

By coming as an honest friend: 'So thick headed', 'so slow hearted;' sometimes we misunderstand who God is when we are anxious and need a fresh perception and understanding of scripture as his disciples did. (*Luke 24:25*)

By coming as the risen Lord: Jesus wants to 'open our eyes' to a new understanding of who He is in the journey with fear and anxiety. (*Luke 24:31*)

Renewed perspective

- Admit to God that you are anxious and believe that God hears the confession of fear and anxious negative thoughts.

- Remember you are not alone. Many Christians have and do battle with anxious negative thoughts.

- Recall how David in Scripture 'lamented' before God: *'Save me, O God! For waters have come up to my neck, I sink in deep mire ...' (Psalm 69)* or *'Hear my voice, O God, in my complaint preserve my life from ...' (Psalm 64)*

- Like David, hold on to the anchor of your life *'But God is my refuge.'*

- Return to the scriptures of Module 1 (I am accepted; I am secure; I am significant)

- Ask His forgiveness for every anxious thought (*1 John1:9*) believing there is no condemnation for those who are in Christ Jesus (*Romans 8:1*)

- Receive God's forgiveness and love. (*Romans 8:39*)

- Continue to replace the negative lies that anxiety whispers into the mind by 'setting' your mind on God's truth (*Philippians 4:8*)

Biblical Antidote to Anxiety

Philippians 4:4-7 provides a Biblical antidote to anxiety:

> *Rejoice in the Lord always. I will say it again: Rejoice!*
> *Let your gentleness be evident to all.*
> *The Lord is near.*
>
> *Do not be anxious about anything.*
> *But in everything by prayer and petition*
> *With thanksgiving*
> *Present your requests to God.*
> *And the peace of God, which transcends all understanding,*
> *will guard your hearts and minds in Christ Jesus.*

In other words, peace is brought through adding praise to prayer.

Praise + Prayer = Peace

Remember that renewing of the mind is a continuous lifelong process for all Christians. It is particularly important to remember when battling with anxious negative thoughts. The Bible encourages believers to be renewed in our minds. (*Ephesians 4:23, Romans 12:2*)

Problem solving

The way we live our lives can have a significant effect on how we feel. A stressful lifestyle can make us feel run down and unable to cope with daily living activities, which in turn increases our anxiety.

As we have realised unhelpful thinking and actions affects our ability to see situations clearly. Thinking negatively increases our worry over problems and then minimises our ability to work out a solution for the problem.

Simple things like how much sleep we get, what we eat and drink and how we solve problems can make a difference to anxiety levels. In the past, problem solving may have been automatic, however anxiety and negative thinking can cause a loss of confidence in solving problems effectively.

Why is it difficult to solve a problem?

Anxiety is a response to perceived threat and triggers the 'flight' or 'fight' response.

Sometimes anxiety is present because there are hidden factors affecting our motivation to solve a problem. Perhaps there is a threat to our self-image or a fear of failure or looking foolish. These can be the basis of many people's anxiety because they perceive a situation that threatens the high expectations they have of themselves personally. The more serious the perceived threat is, the greater the likelihood of anxiety and this inhibits problem solving.

The myth of finding the 'right solution' can inhibit problem solving as can the belief that there is the 'perfect solution'. So often, solutions have pros and cons and there is not one perfect solution.

When considering using the problem solving strategy it is important to choose a 'real' problem rather than an 'unsolvable worry.'

A 'real' problem

A 'real' problem is a problem in the here and now that you have some control over and that requires a solution. For example: You need to pay your road tax and council tax but do not have enough money for both.

An 'unsolvable worry'

An 'unsolvable worry' is an unrealistic and unlikely prediction of the future, over which you have little control. It is not a problem that requires an actual solution. For example: My daughter may become involved in a road accident.

The 6 stages of problem solving

Problem solving is a constructive thought process focused on identifying the problem and effectively thinking of possible ways of dealing with that problem.

Step 1 – Defining the problem

Write down exactly what you believe to be the main problem. Be specific. What is going to happen? When will it happen? Who will be involved?

Problem definition:

....

....

....

Step 2 – List as many solutions as possible

List all the ideas that occur to you, even if they seem silly. Don't evaluate the ideas generated.

List all possible solutions:

1. ....
2. ....
3. ....
4. ....
5. ....

Now eliminate the less desirable or unrealistic solutions. Then list the remaining options in order of preference.

Preferred solutions:

1. ....
2. ....
3. ....
4. ....
5. ....

Step 3 – Evaluate the advantages and disadvantages of each solution

Solution	Advantages	Disadvantages
1		
2		
3		
4		
5		

Step 4 – Select the best and most promising solution

Choose the solution that can most easily be carried out with your present resources; it may help to discuss this with someone you trust.

You may include:

- What will I do?

- How will I do it?

- When will I do it?

- Who else will be involved?

- Where will it take place?

- What do I need for it to happen?

Step 5 – Carry out your chosen solution; implement the plan.

Step 6 – Review and evaluate the outcome

The solution you may have chosen may or may not work perfectly. However it is important to praise your efforts. Decide whether your plan needs to be revised. Has it worked completely, partially or not at all? If not at all you may want to return to Step 2 to select a new option. Continue with the problem solving process until you have resolved the problem. (Be patient and persist.)

The problem solving strategy will need practise and time. When you next have a problem that is in the here and now and is one that you have control over, instead of becoming anxious about it try and use the problem solving strategy.

Summary of module 5

ᛩ The 3 steps of identifying, challenging and balancing negative unhelpful thinking enable us on our journey of handling anxiety.

ᛩ Positive Self-talk and self-praise help build confidence alongside problem-solving techniques to help decision-making.

ᛩ Prayerfully telling God about each anxious thought, reminds us it is a journey of learning with God to 'cast' those anxious thoughts before God and letting His truth renew the anxious mind.

Conclusion

In order to review the modules it is helpful to consider how you are going to progress in the future. This is helped by an honest appraisal of how you are now presently managing your anxiety. It is important to note that you will have good seasons and more difficult seasons. This can be affected by new stress factors, life stages, tiredness, illness or how you presently perceive your personal relationship with Father God?

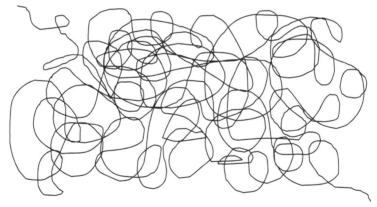

PERSONAL FUTURE ANXIETY MANAGEMENT PLAN

Think back to past situations in which you have felt anxious. Using what you have learned about yourself and your relationship with your heavenly Father it may help you to consider the following as a relapse prevention plan:

Are there future situations that may trigger anxiety?

....

....

....

What are the first signs that I am feeling anxious?

- My physical symptoms:

....

....

....

....

- My behaviours:

....

....

....

....

- My thoughts:

....
....
....
....
....

- My emotions:

....
....
....
....
....
....

- How does my relationship with God alter when I am anxious?

....
....
....
....
....
....

Now remember to consider:

What Safety Behaviours or Avoidance strategy do I revert to when I am anxious?

....
....

....

....

What Thinking Styles do I employ when I am more anxious?

....

....

....

....

How can I intervene at this point to enable myself to manage the anxiety level?

....

....

....

....

How can I manage my physical responses?

....

....

....

....

How can I manage my anxious behaviour?

....

....

....

....

How can I challenge my anxious thoughts?

....

....

....

....

How can I help my relationship with God and enable my prayers not to become worry prayers? Can I pray differently? Review Biblical verses.

....

....

....

....

Who do I need to talk to?

....

What do I need to do to look after myself? (Contact a friend and ask for prayer or contact a GP)

....

....

....

....

It is helpful to continue to recognise our journey with anxiety may be undulating and there may be seasons when we need to review what we have recently learned.

It is encouraging to know that our journey with God is for eternity and He promises to bring to completion the work he has begun!

FURTHER READING SUGGESTIONS

Overcoming Anxiety by Helen Kennerley

Mind Over Mood by Dennis Greenberger & Christine Padesky

Overcoming Panic by Derrick Silove

Spiritual Depression by Lloyd-Jones, D Martyn

Self-help booklets on Cognitive Behavioural Therapy for different conditions by Christopher Williams

OTHER RESOURCES

www.nopanic.org.uk

www.mind.org.uk

www.livinglifetothefull.com

www.nhsdirect.nhs.uk

OTHER READINGS FROM 5 SMOOTH STONES

24 Secrets to Great Parenting

Tried, Tested and True

Jim and Bonnie Inkster

978-0-9563342-0-6

£14.99   Paperback

www.jimandbonnie.co.uk

20-2 Alpha

The Beautiful Struggle

Affi Luc Agbodo

978-0-9563-3421-3

£12.99 Paperback

£7.20   Kindle

www.20-2alpha.co.uk

21720299R10087

Made in the USA
Charleston, SC
05 September 2013